FUN IN THE GULF

Aisha Bowers
and
Leslie P. Engelland

Published with the support and
encouragement of Dubai Duty Free.

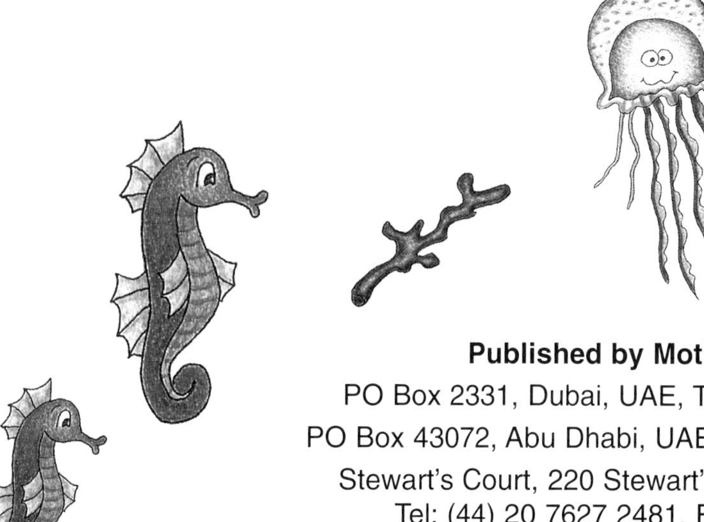

Published by Motivate Publishing

PO Box 2331, Dubai, UAE, Tel: 2824060, Fax: 2824436

PO Box 43072, Abu Dhabi, UAE, Tel: 6271666, Fax: 6271888

Stewart's Court, 220 Stewart's Road, London SW8 4UD,
Tel: (44) 20 7627 2481, Fax: (44) 20 7978 2732

Directors: Obaid Humaid Al Tayer and Ian Fairservice

First Published 1994
First Reprint 1995
Second Reprint 2000

ISBN 1 873544 45 6

British Library Cataloguing-in-Publication Data.
A catalogue record for this book is available from the British Library

Printed by Rashid Printers and Stationers, Ajman, UAE

Titles in the Arabian Heritage Books for Children series:
Fun in the Emirates
Fun in the Gulf

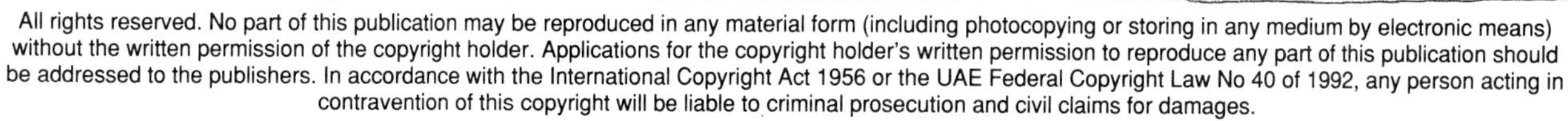

مرحبا

"Marhaba" means "Welcome!" in Arabic.
Welcome to this book about six countries in the Arabian Peninsula.

Arabia is a vast land full of surprises. You'd expect to find camels and desert here, of course – but how about beautiful coral reefs? Fertile green mountains? Farms and dairies and skyscrapers, too!

Find out more about Arabia by turning the pages. You'll have fun while you learn!

PS. To check your answers to any of the puzzles, see pages 42 and 43.

The Arab Gulf Cooperation Council (AGCC) is made up of six countries:

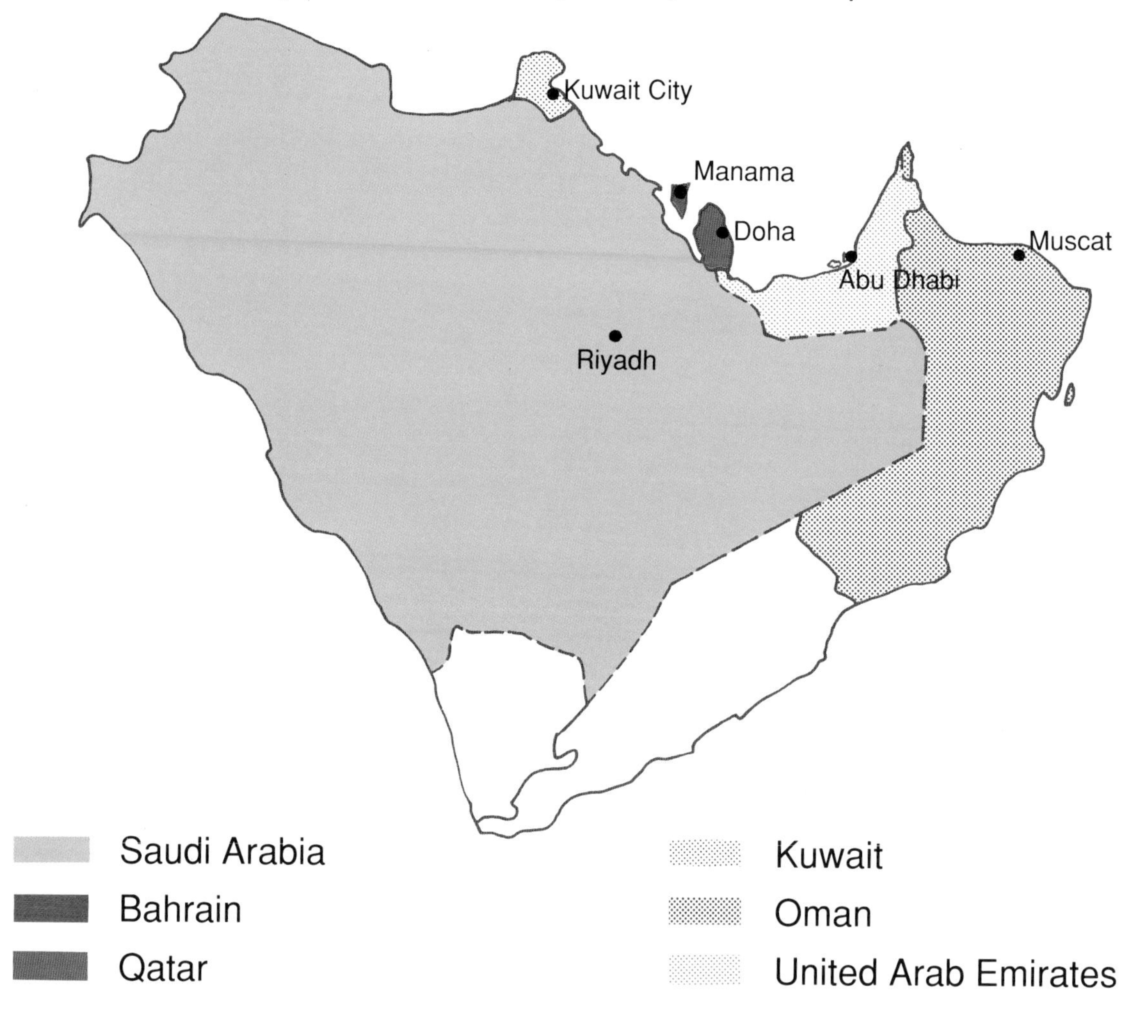

Where do you live? Where have you visited?
Who do you know who lives here?

Match each AGCC country with its capital:

Doha	**United Arab Emirates**
Kuwait City	**Oman**
Riyadh	**Kuwait**
Abu Dhabi	**Qatar**
Manama	**Bahrain**
Muscat	**Saudi Arabia**

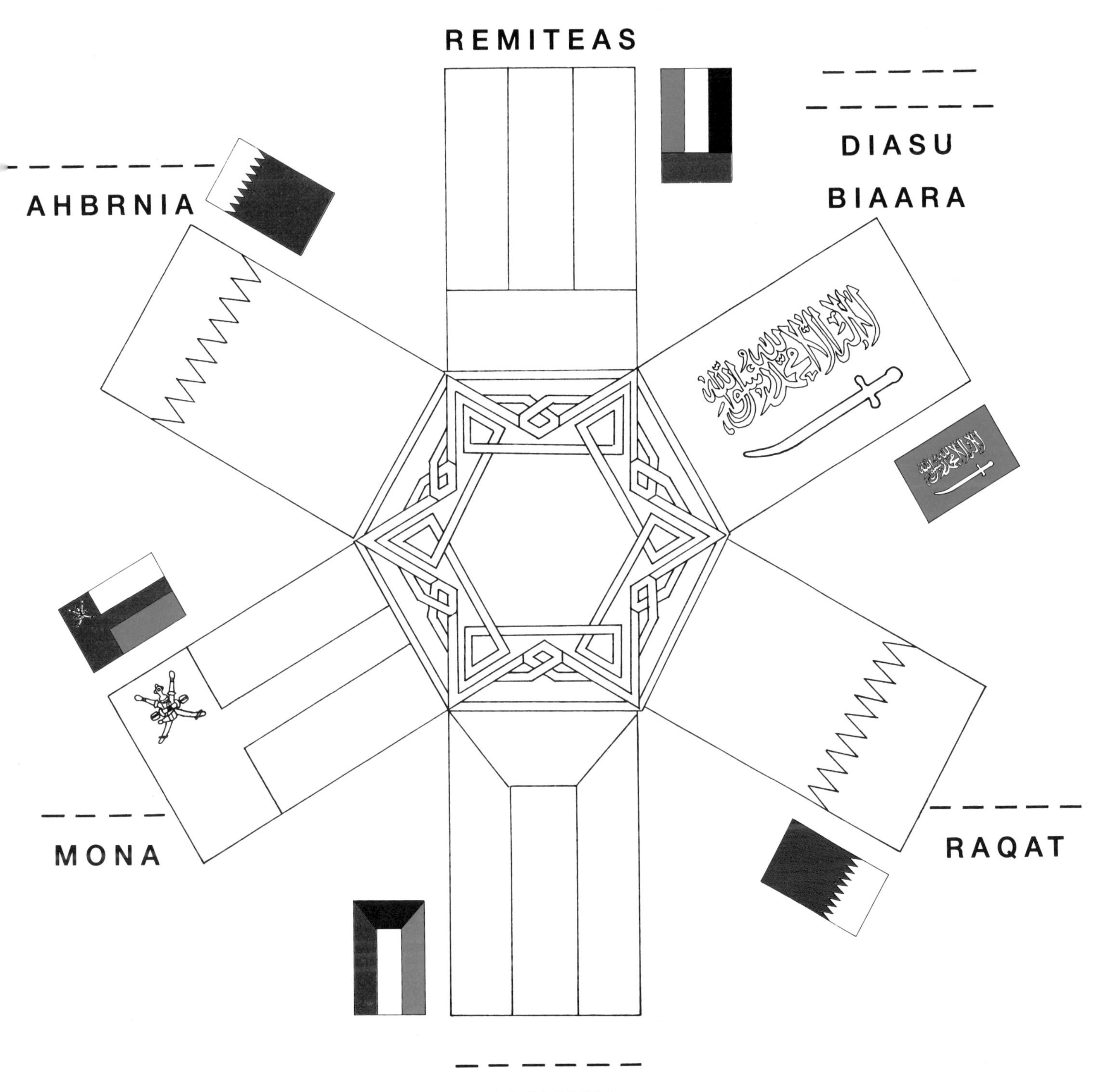

Unscramble the letters to find the names of the six countries which make up the Arab Gulf Cooperation Council.

Samir and his friends are shopping in Dubai Duty Free before leaving on their holiday. What can they buy to keep themselves busy on the flight? How about gifts for Mum and Dad? What do they have to do for a chance to win Dubai Duty Free's Finest Surprise?

llery
Cameras
Books
Dubai Duty Free's Finest Surprise
السوق الحرة - دبي
DUBAI DUTY FREE

Help the seahorse find his way home.

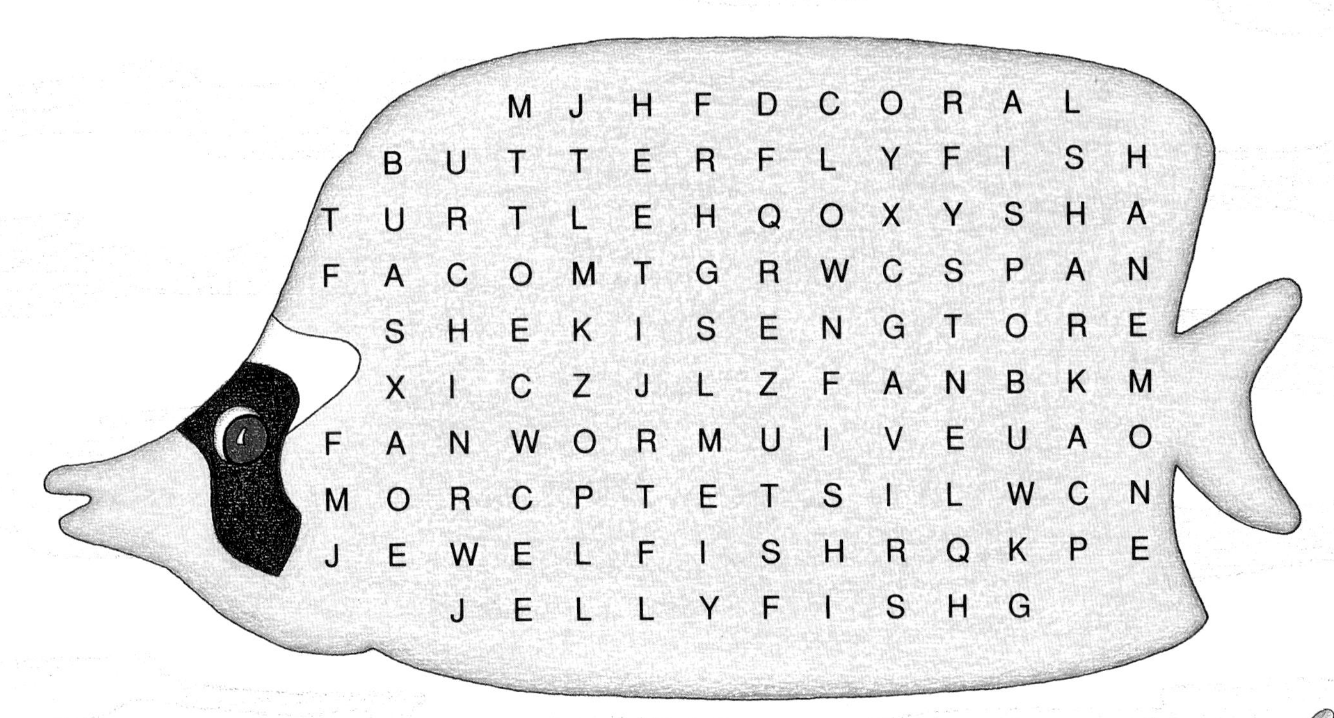

TURTLE

JELLYFISH

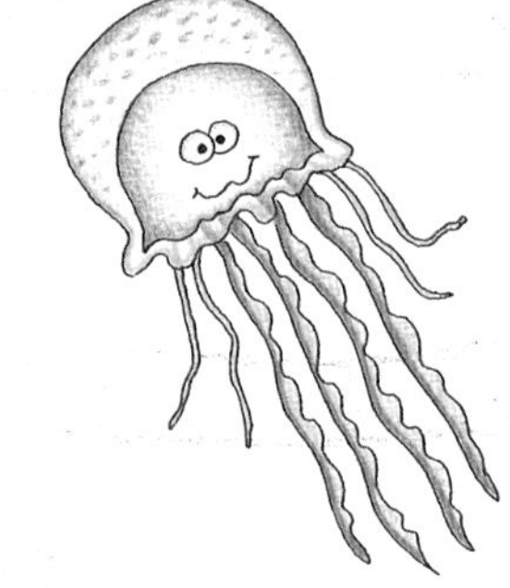

SHARK

CLOWNFISH

BUTTERFLYFISH

JEWELFISH

ANEMONE

URCHIN

FANWORM

An Arabian reef is full of colourful plants and animals.
Can you find their names hidden above?

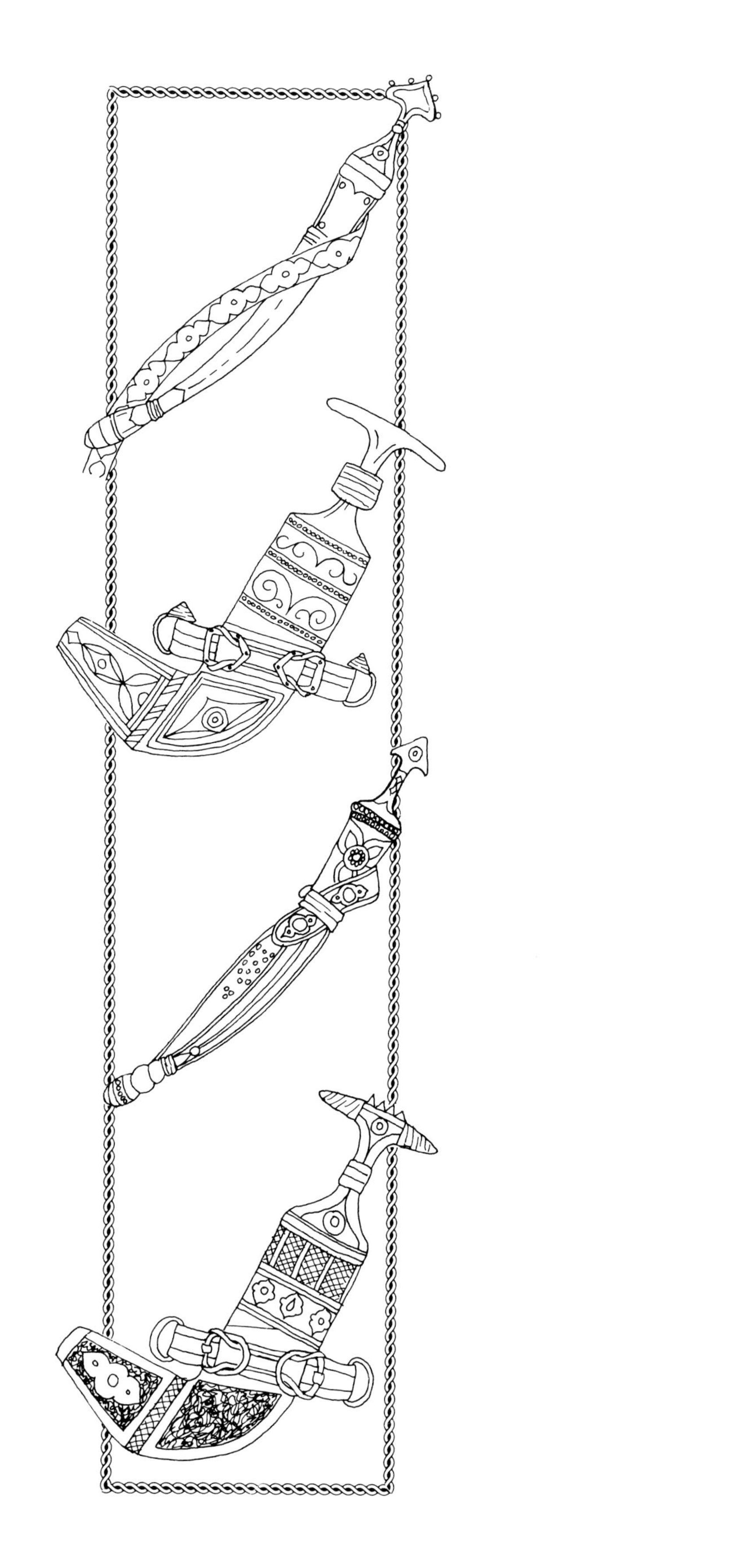

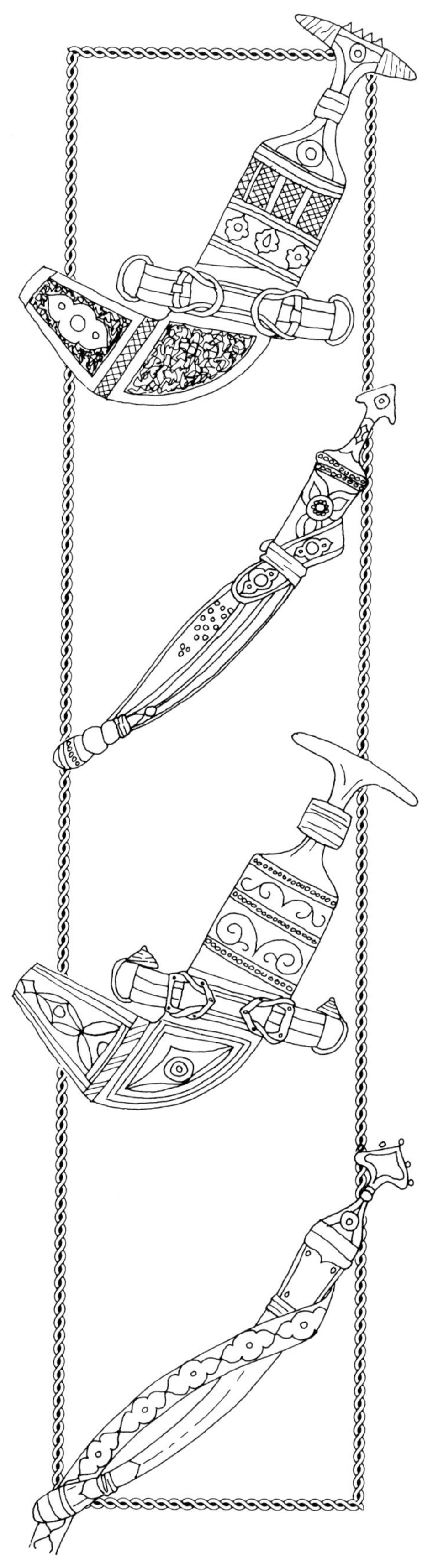

Draw a line between each matching scabbard.

Colour the old fort in Oman.

Ten children are playing in this garden. Can you find them?

What is the name of this animal found in the green mountains of Arabia?
Cross out the letters W,I,L,D below to find out.

Colour the towers of Kuwait.

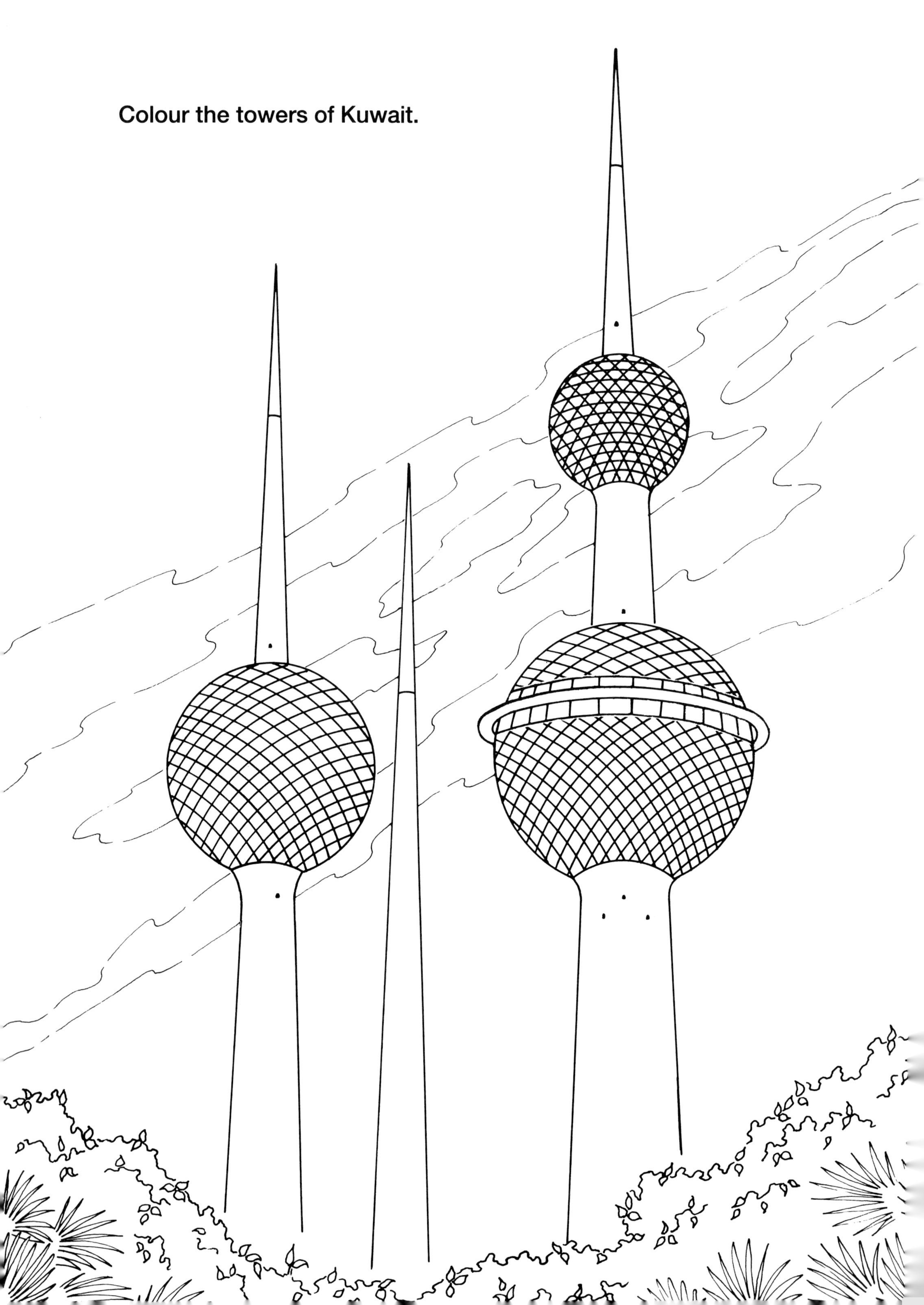

Connect the dots to see a relatively new object in Arabia.

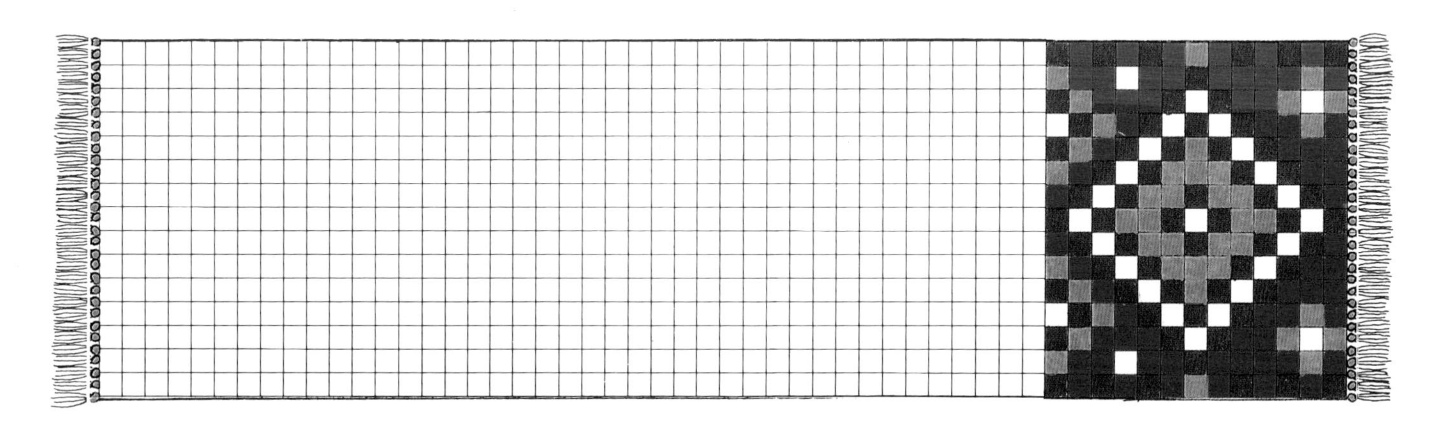

Finish colouring in the pattern on the weaver's loom.

A potter makes many different kinds of pots.
Can you find the two pots that
look exactly alike?

Colour this necklace made of gold, jewels and Arabian pearls.

Which pearl diver (A,B,C) has found the giant pearl? Which diver is wearing the jelly (diving) suit? Which diver is on his way back to the boat?

Colour the old door.

Help Maryam find her way home from the well.

Marhaba! My
My dress is several bri
I am dancing next to my frien
On my other side is another friend,
I am smiling b
Which d

D A S
A E N P
F T O B S
A E Q E
D C S T J
Z N G A B L
A H D D M
R H S A I N
Z B K T Q
D G W J E C
A H N M S
P T E T O Q
R E F K W
F S S N J Y
H O S P S
O M E O E R
D T L T P
U A R A L G
D T D X H
G R E A Z G
H N Y S T S
I O C L E I
D S V O T S
A O D A X V
M T U D F I
U E R C G K
O N S U W Y
D A B M O E
H A S I D T I
W T B B A H
S S E Z D T N
N K S V Q E
I Q E B U S S
R T X J E K
N A M D T P O
D F B A H R
A R Y D T S B
X K W A E H
O P J V T S Y
A U G A E E
A S V D R S S
N K A M I L
How many D-A-T-E-S
do you see in this tree?

Colour this old street in Jeddah, Saudi Arabia.

Colour each space with two dots to see a traditional symbol of Arabian hospitality (or to see something used in Arabia to welcome a guest).

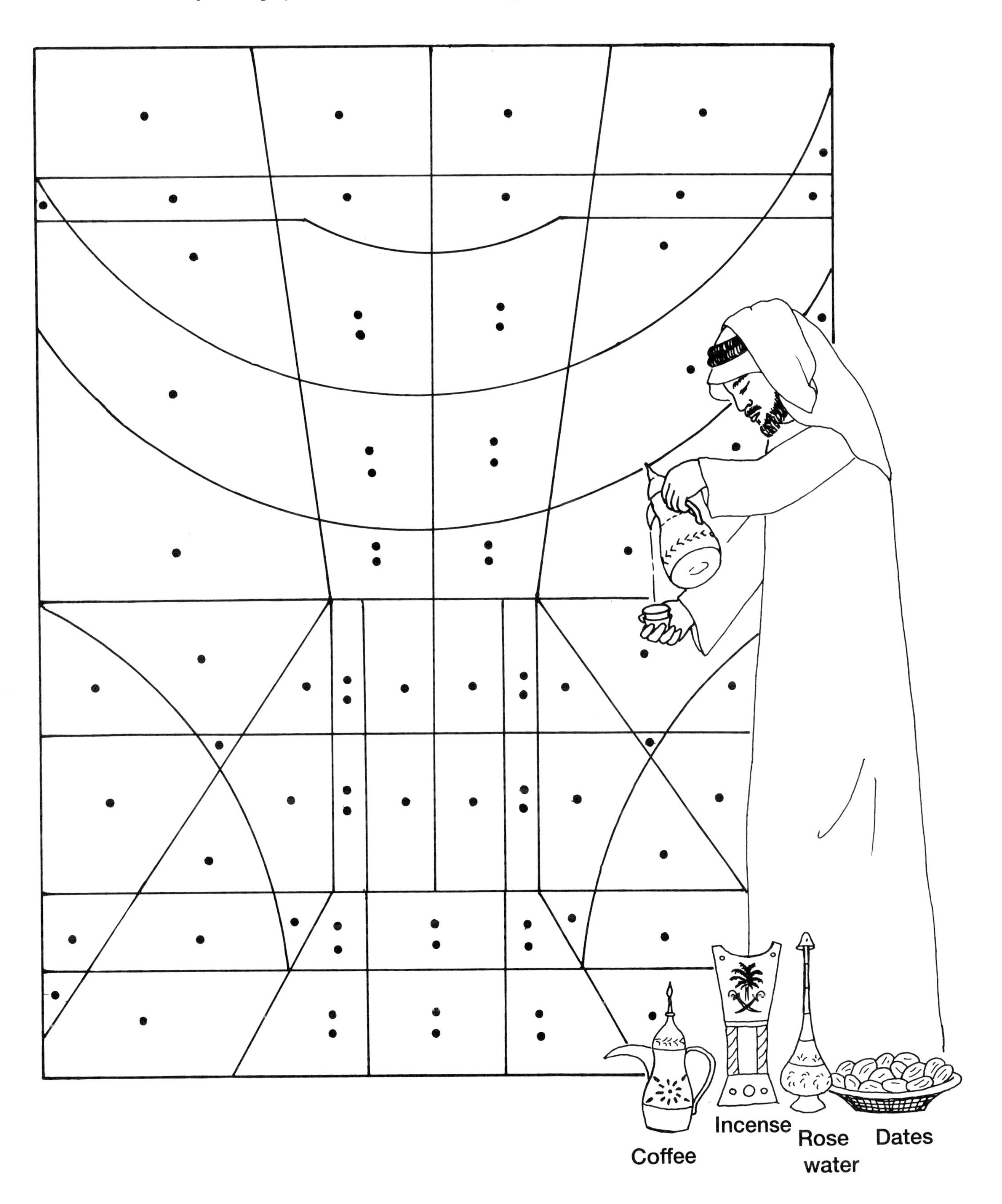

Colour the minarets.

THE FIVE DAILY PRAYERS

Down

1. Sunset Prayer
2. Noon Prayer
4. Mid-Afternoon Prayer

Across

3. Dawn Prayer
5. Night Prayer

Colour the old city gate in Manama, Bahrain.

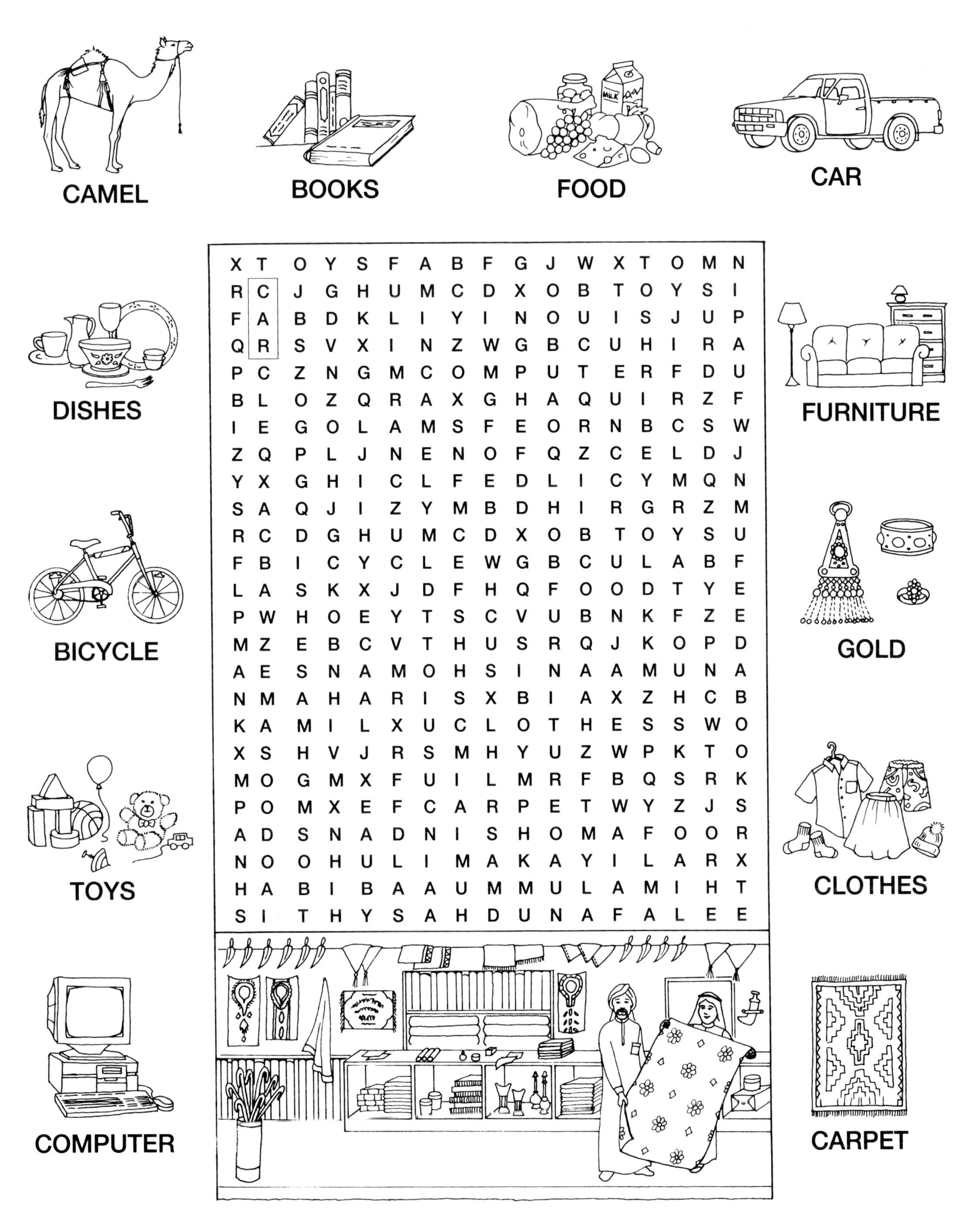

What can you buy in the souks (shopping areas) of Arabia?

Fatimah
cousins & friends
henna
sweets
tea
THE HENNA PARTY
is getting married. One night before the big
wedding celebration,
invites her
to come over
for a
party. They sit on the floor and use
to paint
beautiful patterns and designs on
. Soon swirls, dots, leaves
and flowers drawn in
cover her hands and her feet.
Then, when
is properly decorated, her
take turns and use
to make themselves beautiful, too. They eat
lovely
and drink sweet
throughout the evening.
The whole time
and her
talk and laugh and
make plans for the wedding day. A
party is a very happy time.

Help Ameena prepare
for her wedding.
Draw a henna pattern
on her other hand.

Colour the windtower in Doha, Qatar.

What flies across the desert skies? Connect the dots to find out.

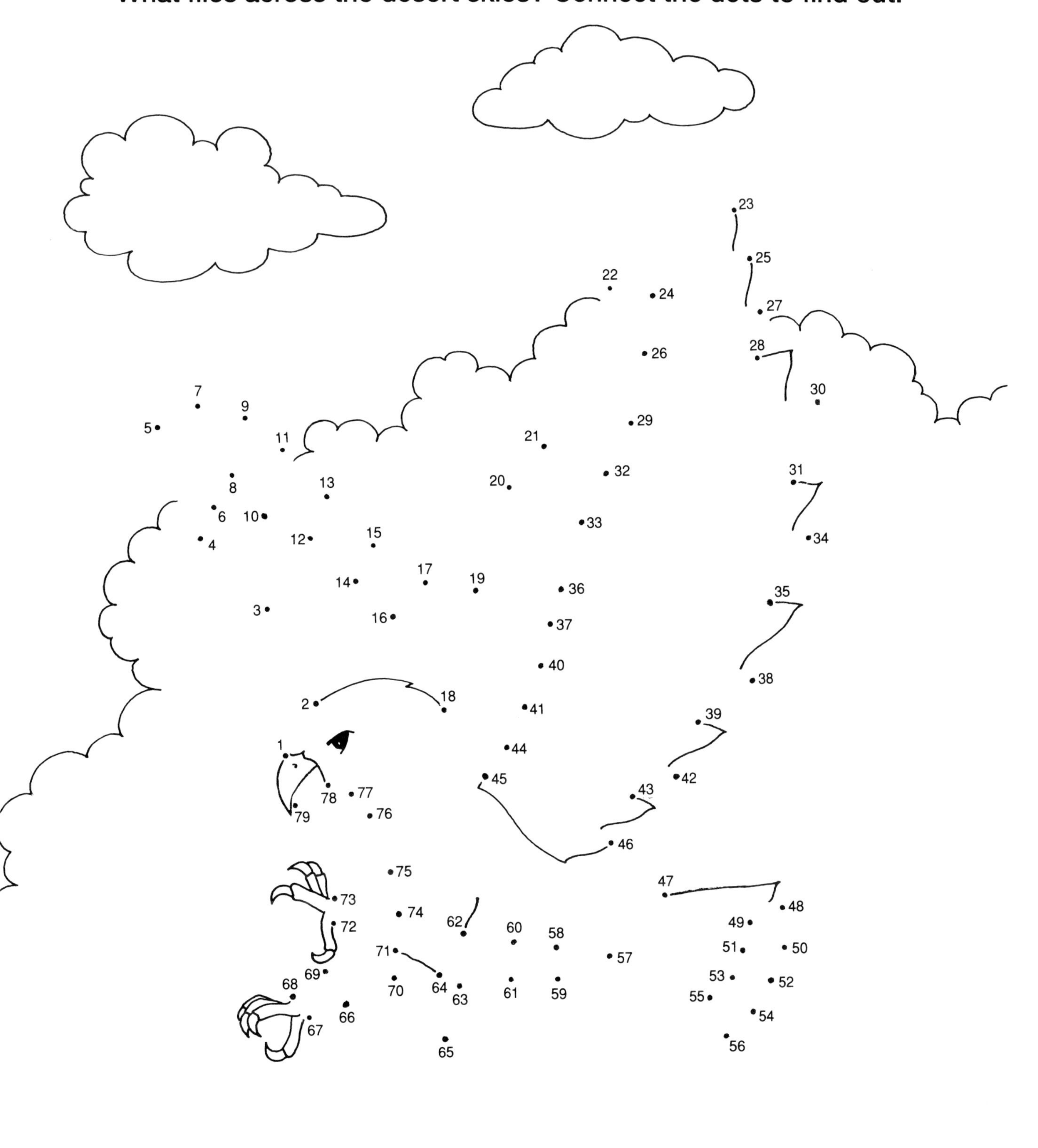

Why can’t you tell jokes to a snake?

Because you can’t pull its leg!

Match each animal with its track.

Help these children from all over the

world find their way to Dubai Duty Free.

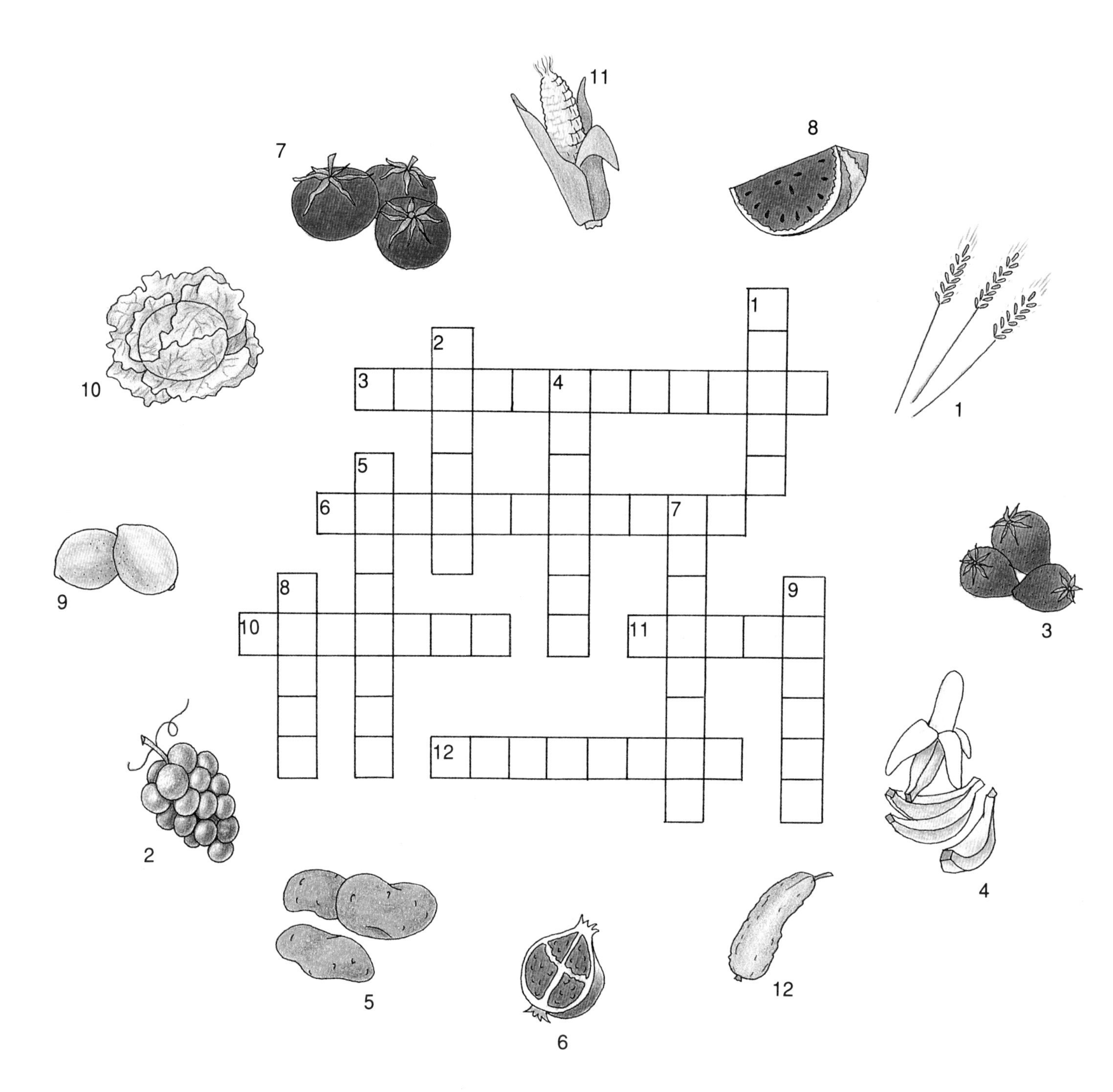

Do you know these fruits, vegetables and grains that are grown in the Arabian Peninsula?

lettuce	cucumber	melon
wheat	strawberries	bananas
maize	lemons	tomatoes
grapes	potatoes	pomegranate

The farmer has lost eight objects that help him with his work.
Can you find a seed package, a hand trowel, a watering can,
a rake, a rope, a glove, a pair of shears and a blade?

Answers

page 4

COUNTRY	CAPITAL
UNITED ARAB EMIRATES	ABU DHABI
OMAN	MUSCAT
KUWAIT	KUWAIT CITY
QATAR	DOHA
BAHRAIN	MANAMA
SAUDI ARABIA	RIYADH

page 5

DETINU AARB REMITEAS = UNITED ARAB EMIRATES
AHBRNIA = BAHRAIN
DIASU BIAARA = SAUDI ARABIA
MONA = OMAN
RAQAT = QATAR
WAKITU = KUWAIT

page 9

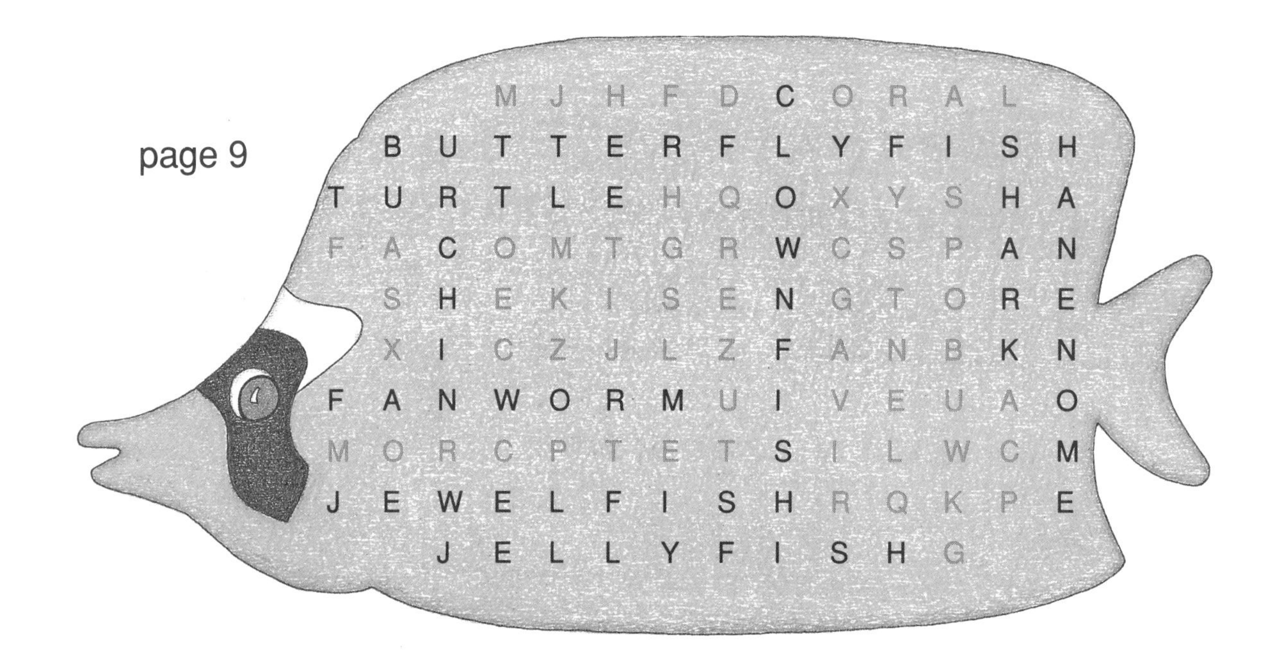

page 29

page 37

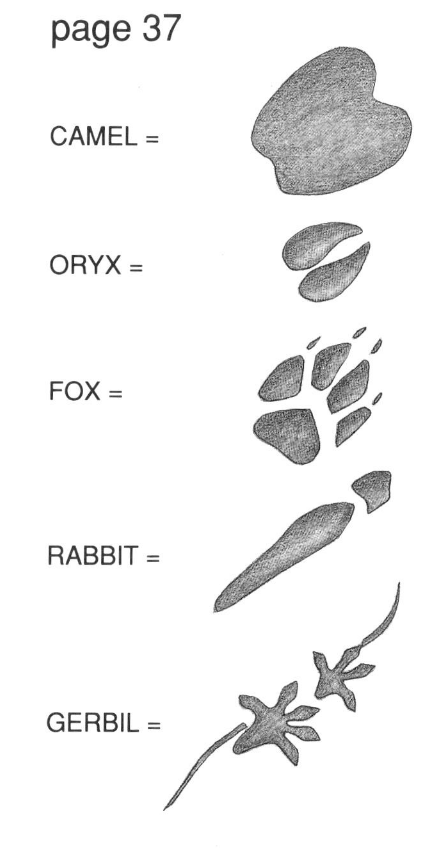

page 31

X	T	O	Y	S	F	A	B	F	G	J	W	X	T	O	M	N
R	C	J	G	H	U	M	C	D	X	O	B	T	O	Y	S	I
F	A	B	D	K	L	I	Y	I	N	O	U	I	S	J	U	P
Q	R	S	V	X	I	N	Z	W	G	B	C	U	H	I	R	A
P	C	Z	N	G	M	C	O	M	P	U	T	E	R	F	D	U
B	L	O	Z	Q	R	A	X	G	H	A	Q	U	I	R	Z	F
I	E	G	O	L	A	M	S	F	E	O	R	N	B	C	S	W
Z	Q	P	L	J	N	E	N	O	F	Q	Z	C	E	L	D	J
Y	X	G	H	I	C	L	F	E	D	L	I	C	Y	M	Q	N
S	A	Q	J	I	Z	Y	M	B	D	H	I	R	G	R	Z	M
R	C	D	G	H	U	M	C	D	X	O	B	T	O	Y	S	U
F	B	I	C	Y	C	L	E	W	G	B	C	U	L	A	B	F
L	A	S	K	X	J	D	F	H	Q	F	O	O	D	T	Y	E
P	W	H	O	E	Y	T	S	C	V	U	B	N	K	F	Z	E
M	Z	E	B	C	V	T	H	U	S	R	Q	J	K	O	P	D
A	E	S	N	A	M	O	H	S	I	N	A	A	M	U	N	A
N	M	A	H	A	R	I	S	X	B	I	A	X	Z	H	C	B
K	A	M	I	L	X	U	C	L	O	T	H	E	S	S	W	O
X	S	H	V	J	R	S	M	H	Y	U	Z	W	P	K	T	O
M	O	G	M	X	F	U	I	L	M	R	F	B	Q	S	R	K
P	O	M	X	E	F	C	A	R	P	E	T	W	Y	Z	J	S
A	D	S	N	A	D	N	I	S	H	O	M	A	F	O	O	R
N	O	O	H	U	L	I	M	A	K	A	Y	I	L	A	R	X
H	A	B	I	B	A	A	U	M	M	U	L	A	M	I	H	T
S	I	T	H	Y	S	A	H	D	U	N	A	F	A	L	E	E

page 25

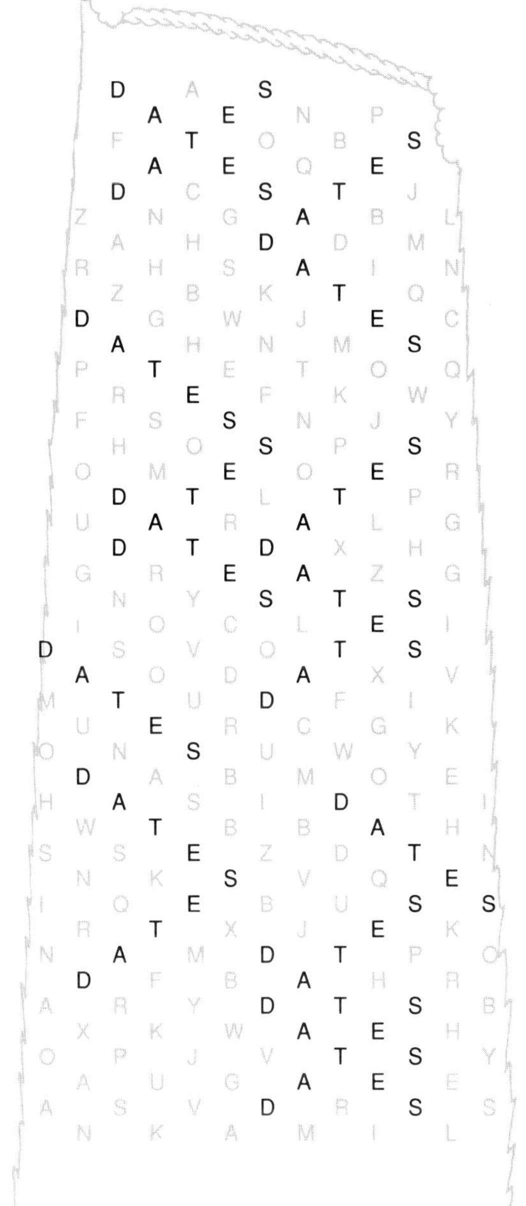

There are 18 D-A-T-E-S

page 40

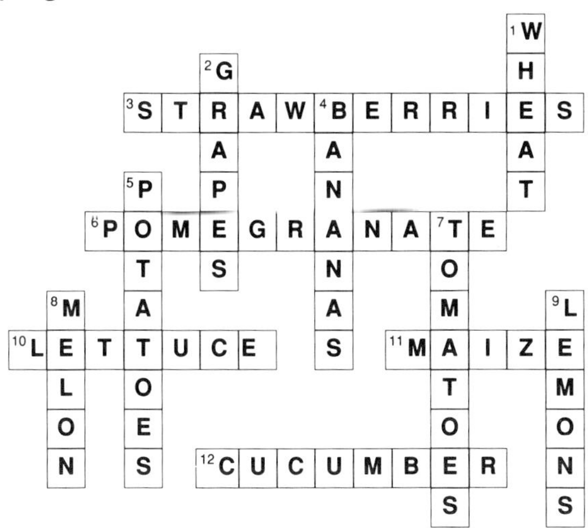

page 22-23
I am the third dancer from the right.

We hope you enjoyed your trip through Arabia. If you're still curious about this marvellous place and want to learn more, ask your Mum or Dad for other books about any of the AGCC countries. You'll find plenty of interesting things to read about!

Ma'asalaama! مع السلامة

Good–bye!

The publishers would like to express their appreciation to the Dubai Duty Free Shopping Complex, whose sponsorship support has made possible the publication of this book.